Conten

My Fab Self

Name:..

Address:..

....

....

Telephone:..

Mobile:...

Email:..

My birthday (vair, vair important!):..............................

....

My best friends (Ace Gang!):......................................

....

....

My most embarrassing moment:......................................

....

....

....

My besty music/bands:..

....

....

My besty ringtones:..

....

My bestest shops:..

....

....

....

My bestiest film:..

....

My bestiestissimus book:..

....

....

My grooviest dream job:..

....

....

....

....

January

A merry New Year to one and all!!!
This year I will mostly be...

_____

_____

_____

_____

_____

_____

_____

_____

_____

_____

_____

_____

_____

_____

_____

_____

February

It's the pucker-up season! So gird
your loins for the Snog Fest!

Year Planarama
March

Ah yes, March, famous for its,
erm, well... madnosity!

_____

_____

_____

_____

_____

_____

_____

_____

_____

_____

_____

_____

_____

_____

_____

_____

Year Planarama
April
Beware the fools!

May

May the 4th be with you

_____

_____

_____

_____

_____

_____

_____

_____

_____

_____

_____

_____

_____

_____

_____

_____

Year Planarama
June

As our Froggy friends say, it's Juin.
But who cares what they dit?

July

At last, the beautiful English summer.
Lovely, lovely drizzly rain! And fog.

_____

_____

_____

_____

_____

_____

_____

_____

_____

_____

_____

_____

_____

_____

_____

_____

_____

Year Planarama
August

Summer hols – I can hear the call
of the Costa del Fiasco.

Year Planarama

September

Back to Stalag 14 - boo, merde
and poo.

October

Cor, it's getting a bit nippy noodles!
Get out your ginormous winter panties.

November

Hurray, Bonfire Night! An ideal opportunity for your dad to set fire to his trousers.

_____

_____

_____

_____

_____

_____

_____

_____

_____

_____

_____

_____

_____

_____

_____

_____

_____

December

Sound out the bells of England,
it's the Chrimboli hols!

To Do List

The vair, vair important things to do...
1. Get up.

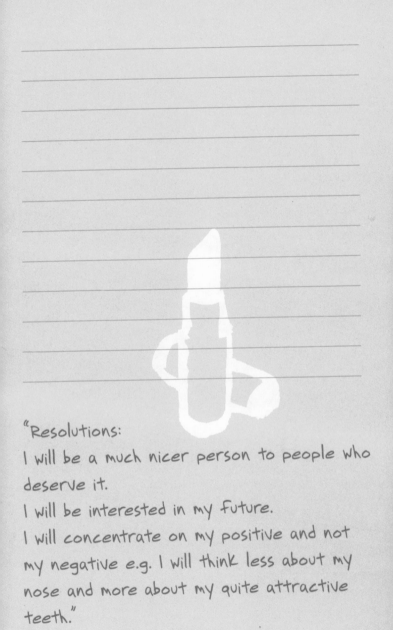

"Resolutions:

I will be a much nicer person to people who deserve it.

I will be interested in my future.

I will concentrate on my positive and not my negative e.g. I will think less about my nose and more about my quite attractive teeth."

To Do List

"I shouted down, 'Thank you, Papa, I'll be down immediately to entertain you with my piano playing.' We haven't got a piano, but it's the thought that counts."

To Do List

"I looked out of the window as I did my alternate nostril breathing. It is vair calming, but I hope it's not like body building. I don't want to be really calm and have massive nostrils."

To Do List

"Rightio. Part two of my luuurve plan. Running begins."

To Do List

"I'm going to be vegetarian... But what about the little baby potatoes, all snug underground. And then a big hand comes and uproots them and slices them up. What can I eat, then?"

Pal Facts

For my nearest and dearest marvy mates.

Name:...
Address:...
....
Telephone:..
Mobile:...
Email:...

Name:...
Address:...
....
Telephone:..
Mobile:...
Email:...

Name:...
Address:...
....
Telephone:..
Mobile:...
Email:...

B

Name:...

Address:...

....

Telephone:...

Mobile:..

Email:..

Name:...

Address:...

....

Telephone:...

Mobile:..

Email:..

Name:...

Address:...

....

Telephone:...

Mobile:..

Email:..

C

Name:..

Address:..

....

Telephone:...

Mobile:..

Email:..

Name:..

Address:..

....

Telephone:...

Mobile:..

Email:..

Name:..

Address:..

....

Telephone:...

Mobile:..

Email:..

D

Name:...
Address:..
....
Telephone:..
Mobile:...
Email:...

Name:...
Address:..
....
Telephone:..
Mobile:...
Email:...

Name:...
Address:..
....
Telephone:..
Mobile:...
Email:...

E

Name:...
Address:...
....
Telephone:...
Mobile:..
Email:...

Name:...
Address:...
....
Telephone:...
Mobile:..
Email:...

Name:...
Address:...
....
Telephone:...
Mobile:..
Email:...

G

Name:...
Address:...
....
Telephone:..
Mobile:...
Email:...

Name:...
Address:...
....
Telephone:..
Mobile:...
Email:...

Name:...
Address:...
....
Telephone:..
Mobile:...
Email:...

G

Name:..
Address:..
....
Telephone:..
Mobile:..
Email:..

Name:..
Address:..
....
Telephone:..
Mobile:..
Email:..

Name:..
Address:..
....
Telephone:..
Mobile:..
Email:..

H

Name:...
Address:...
....
Telephone:...
Mobile:..
Email:..

Name:...
Address:...
....
Telephone:...
Mobile:..
Email:..

Name:...
Address:...
....
Telephone:...
Mobile:..
Email:..

9

Name:..
Address:..
....
Telephone:..
Mobile:...
Email:...

Name:..
Address:..
....
Telephone:..
Mobile:...
Email:...

Name:..
Address:..
....
Telephone:..
Mobile:...
Email:...

J

Name:..
Address:..
....
Telephone:..
Mobile:...
Email:...

Name:..
Address:..
....
Telephone:..
Mobile:...
Email:...

Name:..
Address:..
....
Telephone:..
Mobile:...
Email:...

K

Name:..
Address:..
....
Telephone:..
Mobile:...
Email:...

Name:..
Address:..
....
Telephone:..
Mobile:...
Email:...

Name:..
Address:..
....
Telephone:..
Mobile:...
Email:...

Name:..
Address:..
....
Telephone:..
Mobile:...
Email:...

Name:..
Address:..
....
Telephone:..
Mobile:...
Email:...

Name:..
Address:..
....
Telephone:..
Mobile:...
Email:...

M

Name:..

Address:..

....

Telephone:..

Mobile:...

Email:...

Name:..

Address:..

....

Telephone:..

Mobile:...

Email:...

Name:..

Address:..

....

Telephone:..

Mobile:...

Email:...

N

Name:..
Address:..
....
Telephone:...
Mobile:...
Email:...

Name:..
Address:..
....
Telephone:...
Mobile:...
Email:...

Name:..
Address:..
....
Telephone:...
Mobile:...
Email:...

Name:...
Address:...
....
Telephone:...
Mobile:..
Email:...

Name:...
Address:...
....
Telephone:...
Mobile:..
Email:...

Name:...
Address:...
....
Telephone:...
Mobile:..
Email:...

P

Name:...
Address:...
....
Telephone:..
Mobile:...
Email:...

Name:...
Address:...
....
Telephone:..
Mobile:...
Email:...

Name:...
Address:...
....
Telephone:..
Mobile:...
Email:...

Q

Name:..
Address:..
....
Telephone:..
Mobile:...
Email:..

Name:..
Address:..
....
Telephone:..
Mobile:...
Email:..

Name:..
Address:..
....
Telephone:..
Mobile:...
Email:..

R

Name:...
Address:...
....
Telephone:..
Mobile:..
Email:..

Name:...
Address:...
....
Telephone:..
Mobile:..
Email:..

Name:...
Address:...
....
Telephone:..
Mobile:..
Email:..

Pals

S

Name:..

Address:..

....

Telephone:...

Mobile:..

Email:..

Name:..

Address:..

....

Telephone:...

Mobile:..

Email:..

Name:..

Address:..

....

Telephone:...

Mobile:..

Email:..

T

Name:..
Address:..
....
Telephone:...
Mobile:..
Email:...

Name:..
Address:..
....
Telephone:...
Mobile:..
Email:...

Name:..
Address:..
....
Telephone:...
Mobile:..
Email:...

U

Name:..

Address:..

....

Telephone:...

Mobile:...

Email:..

Name:..

Address:..

....

Telephone:...

Mobile:...

Email:..

Name:..

Address:..

....

Telephone:...

Mobile:...

Email:..

V

Name:...

Address:..

....

Telephone:..

Mobile:..

Email:..

Name:...

Address:..

....

Telephone:..

Mobile:..

Email:..

Name:...

Address:..

....

Telephone:..

Mobile:..

Email:..

W

Name:...

Address:...

....

Telephone:...

Mobile:..

Email:..

Name:...

Address:...

....

Telephone:...

Mobile:..

Email:..

Name:...

Address:...

....

Telephone:...

Mobile:..

Email:..

X

Name:..
Address:..
....
Telephone:...
Mobile:..
Email:..

Name:..
Address:..
....
Telephone:...
Mobile:..
Email:..

Name:..
Address:..
....
Telephone:...
Mobile:..
Email:..

U

Name:...
Address:...
....
Telephone:...
Mobile:..
Email:...

Name:...
Address:...
....
Telephone:...
Mobile:..
Email:...

Name:...
Address:...
....
Telephone:...
Mobile:..
Email:...

Z

Name:...
Address:...
....
Telephone:...
Mobile:...
Email:...

Name:...
Address:...
....
Telephone:...
Mobile:...
Email:...

Name:...
Address:...
....
Telephone:...
Mobile:...
Email:...

Birthdays of m...

January

_____

February

_____

March

_____

April

_____

May

_____

June

Fabbity Friends

Je ne forget pas!

July

_____

August

_____

September

_____

October

_____

November

_____

December

_____

Birthday Prezzies

If Mutti and Vati **really** luuurved me
they would get me...

_____

_____

_____

_____

_____

_____

_____

_____

_____

_____

_____

_____

_____

_____

_____

_____

_____

"Mum said, 'Dad phoned again... he's got you a present.' I said, 'Oh goodie, what is it? Sheepskin shorts?'"

Clothes & Accessories

Stuff that I want fashionwise...

_____
_____
_____
_____
_____
_____
_____
_____
_____
_____
_____
_____
_____
_____
_____
_____
_____
_____
_____
_____

"I thought I'd wear my pencil-line skirt the first day back, with hold-up stockings and my ankle boots."

Clothes & Accessories

"I am in a state of confusiosity. Why are my parents too mean to get me a style counsellor?"

Clothes & Accessories

"I'm wearing a V-necked black leather vest, short skirt and boots. What does that say about me? Casual sophisticate? Inner vixen struggling to get out? Girlfriend of a Sex God? Or twit?"

Clothes & Accessories

Wish Lists

"WHAT ON EARTH CAN I WEAR???"

Clothes & Accessories

"I am truly a BABE magnet. Even in my
Teletubbies jimjams."

Make-up & Beauty

Make-up wise, lighten up! Go natural.
But having said that, don't go mad – natural
doesn't mean really really plain.

_____
_____
_____
_____
_____
_____
_____
_____
_____
_____
_____
_____
_____
_____
_____

"It takes most of the day to achieve my natural make-up look. Just a subtle touch to enhance my natural beauty."

Make-up & Beauty

"For the just-tumbled-out-of-bed look I only use concealer, foundation, a hint of bronzer, eye pencil, mascara, lip liner, lippy and lip gloss, and leave it at that."

Make-up & Beauty

"Even though I have been through the mangle of love and beyond, I can still be bothered to cleanse and tone."

Make-up & Beauty

"It's incredibly nippy noodles but at least my face is snug. It should be – it has several layers of make-up on it."

Beauty Hints From Mags

Checklist:
1. nail varnish remover
2. lurker remover

"Time for my pore-tightening mask (because there is nothing worse than loose pores)."

Beauty Hints From Mags

"Pluck for England so that you do not have just the one eyebrow across your forehead."

Beauty Hints From Mags

"It is vair important to check the back of your legs too – if you don't want a baboon effect rear-wise."

Poptastic Tunes

Current fave bands...

"What is silly about disco dancing?"

Poptastic Tunes

Grooviest looking pop hunks
and smooth movers...

"He was so gorgey and a fantasadosy
singer and soooooo sexy."

Poptastic Tunes

Fabbest lyrics...

"I had to go to bed because Vati was singing 'I Will Always Love Youuuuuuuuuuuuu' by Whitney Useless."

Give me what I want now!

Places to go...

Gigs and shows to go to...

"Escape!! Freedom!!! Party!!!!"

Give me what I want now!

My ideal day...

_____

_____

_____

_____

_____

_____

_____

_____

_____

_____

_____

_____

_____

_____

_____

_____

_____

_____

"In principle I think parents should really only be like sort of human purses."

Give me what I want now!

Stuff for my room...

_____

_____

_____

_____

_____

_____

_____

_____

_____

_____

_____

_____

_____

_____

_____

_____

_____

_____

_____

Famous people to meet...

"Ohmygiddygodstrousers, he was absolutely gorgeous! Really really gorgey. Really gorgey! And I do mean gorgey. That's why I said it."

Boys, also known as Sex Gods, Luuurve Gods & Twits

Cosmic Horn confessional time

"I wonder if it is possible to have two
boyfriends? I mean, times are changing.
Relationships are more complicated."

Boys, also known as Sex Gods, Luuurve Gods & Twits

Wish Lists

"The Sex God has landed."

Boys, also known as Sex Gods, Luuurve Gods & Twits

"Apparently girls like boys to say stuff like "you are the most beautiful girl in the world" and boys like you to go "Uummm" and "Oooohh"."

Boys, also known as Sex Gods, Luuurve Gods & Twits

"It is vair vair tiring this boy bananas."

Top Secret: Cosmic
Horn Notes
Oo-er...

The Ace Gang's Snogging Scale

$1/2$. sticky eyes
1. holding hands
2. arm around
3. goodnight kiss
4. kiss lasting over three minutes without a breath
5. open mouth kissing
6. tongues
$6^1/2$ ear snogging
$6^3/4$ neck nuzzling
7. upper body fondling – outdoors
8. upper body fondling – indoors (in bed)
9. below waist activity
10. the full monty

Top Secret: Cosmic Horn Notes

"I am so nervous... What if I have forgotten how to snog? What if all my snogging lessons go out of my mind at the last minute and we bump teeth?"

Top Secret: Cosmic Horn Notes

"I said politely to the lady, 'Have you got a horn?' And that set the gang off in hysterics."

Top Secret: Cosmic Horn Notes

"I had the Particular and Cosmic Horns and a heavy dose of red-bottomosity."

Creativitosity & Geniosity

or rubbish in my head

"Shall I have glaciosity or shall I have boldnosity? What botty huggers shall I wear?"

_____

_____

_____

_____

_____

_____

_____

_____

_____

_____

_____

_____

_____

_____

_____

_____

_____

_____

"You know when you should stop laughing because someone's going to kill you if you don't, but you still keep on? Well, I had that."

_____

_____

_____

_____

_____

_____

_____

_____

_____

_____

_____

_____

_____

_____

"What do I think? What does he mean,
what do I think? How should I know?
If anyone knows what I think it won't
be me. I, of course, will be the last to know."

"I didn't seem to be able to make anything come out of my mouth that had anything to do with my brain."

Creativitosity & Geniosity

"Jas, my so-called besty, can be like half girl, half turnip."

_____

_____

_____

_____

_____

_____

_____

_____

_____

_____

_____

_____

_____

_____

_____

"I have no talent for tidying. Mum thinks
that I deliberately ignore the obvious things
but the truth is I can't tell the difference
between tidy and not tidy."

"I feel like a bean in a bikini, tossed around on the sea of life. Set apart from my mates because of heartbreakosity."

"Anyway, where was I before I so rudely interrupted myself?"

Creativitosity & Geniosity

"Miss Wilson is not what you might call normal (still, who would be, teaching RE?). She is a very unfortunate person with ginger hair in a sad bob, and she wears tragic cardigans, usually done up the wrong way."

Journal ♡

"Dad, or the Portly One, is growing a moustache.
How sad. It looks like some small animal is
having a bit of a sleep on his top lip."

"What does it mean when a boy rests his hand on your basooma? Does it mean he has the mega-horn? Or was his hand just tired?"

_____

_____

_____

_____

_____

_____

_____

_____

_____

_____

_____

_____

_____

_____

_____

_____

_____

"Full-frontal snogging is kissing with all the trimmings: lip to lip, open mouth, tongues, everything. Well, apart from dribble, which is never acceptable."

Creativitosity & Geniosity

"I have no friends. No one has rung. I may as well be dead. If you died in your sleep and woke up dead, who would let you know?"

Rubbish in my Head

"Looking through the family albums I'm not really surprised I'm ugly. The photos of Dad as a child are terrifying."

"If dolphins are so intelligent why don't they learn to speak properly? Instead of squeaking?"

More Rubbish in my Head

_____

_____

_____

_____

_____

_____

_____

_____

_____

_____

_____

_____

_____

_____

_____

_____

_____

"What's the matter with my life? Why is it so deeply unfab?"

Creativitosity & Geniosity

"My cat, Angus, has pooed in Vati's tie drawer! Hilarious really. El Beardo, as usual, did not see the joke."

More Rubbish in my Head

"Oh Blimey O'Reilley's pantyhose, what is the point of Shakespeare? I know he is a genius and so on, but he does rave on."

Creativitosity & Geniosity

"I am so depressed and bored I may even have to do some homework."

"Our revered headmistress 'Slim' Simpson (so called because she weighs about a ton) shook herself. She always did it when she was irritated with us (i.e. all the time). It made her look like a jelly with shoes on."

Creativitosity & Geniosity

"I am beyond the Valley of the Confused and treading lightly in the Universe of the Severely Deranged."

"Angus has eaten some of Mum's knickers. She says he'll have to go. Why can't she go, and Dad go? Or am I being unreasonable?"

Creativitosity & Geniosity

"Biology, double maths, Froggie and geoggers.
Qu-est que le point?"

"Why oh why did this happen to me? I must have done something incredibly bad in a past life."

Creativitosity & Geniosity

"Talking of basoomas, I'm worried I may end up like Mum, with just the one bust like a sort of shelf affair."

More Rubbish in my Head

"Jas, your spaceship has arrived. Please get in."

Creativitosity & Geniosity

"Stop looking at me in that lookingy way."

"I think I may be hysterical with love."

"By the time I count to one hundred in French, the phone will ring. And it will be him. The Sex God."

Even More Rubbish in my Head

"Up at the crack of midday!"

"It was the Sex God at my door. Looking like a Sex God. At my door. The Sex God had landed at my door. I was wearing my Teletubbies pyjamas."

"Night-night, Sex God, wherever you are."

"I may freeze to death, but I will look fabbity fab fab."

Even More Rubbish in my Head

"That is it. My life is over. I must go to the ugly home immediately."

"I hate Sundays. They are deliberately invented by people who have no life and no friends."

Even More Rubbish in my Head

Creativitosity & Geniosity

"On the topic of snog-proof make-up, Jas only wears lip gloss, which she says gets absorbed in the general snoggosity."

"I would rather eat my own poo than be Wet Lindsay's mate. She's a slimy twit with the smallest forehead known to humanity."

Journal

Creativitosity & Geniosity

"Mucho excitemondo and jelly knickers activity!"

"Oh hell's biscuits. Pucker alert, pucker alert!!"

Creativitosity & Geniosity

"I am almost full of wisdomosity. If I can just figure out what in the name of arse I am on about."

Journal ♡

Groovy Websites

www.georgianicolson.com

www.sugarmagazine.co.uk

www.mykindofplace.co.uk

www.asos.com

www.play.com

www.claires.com

www.getlippy.com

www.topshop.co.uk

www.ebay.co.uk

www.google.co.uk

www.itunes.co.uk

www.myspace.com

www.neopets.com

www.msn.co.uk

www.popbeauty.co.uk

www.imdb.com

- le coolest website on the Internet
- the magazine for fab chicks
- tres megafab virtual place to be
- celeb style without the freaky deaky prices!
- tune-arama
- glam me up to Glamland
- gossip-a-gogo
- shopping heavenosity
- bargainosity-a-gogo
- they seriously know where everything on the web is
- poptastic downloads
- blogtastic
- virtual Angus – scary bananas
- Chat for England
- lip glossnosity
- Find out everything about your gorgey fave filmstars

Even More Rubbish in my Head

"I am treading lightly in the Universe of the Very Nearly Quite Happy."